THE STORY OF JESUS

Once, long ago, a gentle young girl called was at home in Nazareth when an visited her. The 's name was Gabriel and he told that God had sent him. "You will have a ," the said. "His name will be Jesus, Son of God."

was engaged to marry a

carpenter who lived in the same

town. His name was and after

they were married liked to

watch at work. might

be busy making a or mending

a wooden for a cart but he

always had time for

 was soon to have her

and was very worried

when he heard that he must take

 to Bethlehem. "We must all

go," he said, "to be counted. The

 commands it."

"I will get some food ready for the

journey," said.

When everything was ready they

set out, seated on a .

What crowds there were in

Bethlehem! It was growing dark and

 had still not found a room.

He could see how tired was.

She could scarcely sit upright on the

 .

Then at last 's luck changed.

A kind-hearted offered them

his stable. Thankfully accepted.

The stable was warm and the
animals there, the big heavy
and the sleepy , were quiet and
friendly.

That night Jesus was born

and wrapped him in

swaddling clothes. filled the

 with clean straw so that

could lay him there.

In the morning some came

to the stable. When they saw the

 in the , wrapped in

swaddling clothes, they were filled

with joy. "It is just as the

said," one whispered. "He is

Christ the Lord!"

A bright new in the East

was a sign to three that a new

 had been born.

The followed the

through many lands until, at last,

they found the Jesus in

Bethlehem. They bowed low before

him and offered the the

they had chosen to be fit for a great

. Then they mounted their

 and rode swiftly away back to

their own land.

did not take his little family

back to Nazareth. Instead he took

the and his mother to Egypt

where they would be safe from the

wicked Herod.

Herod had tried to find

the holy child so that he could have

him killed. But had been

warned in a dream to leave

Bethlehem before Herod's

could discover where they lived.

When the wicked died they

went back to Nazareth.

 grew up in Nazareth. He

went to school like the other boys

and when he was grown-up he

became a carpenter like .

Sometimes talked to the

 on the shore of the Lake of

Galilee. told them about the

Kingdom of Heaven as they sat by

their mending their .

Two of the were brothers.

They wanted very much to try and

be like . "We will follow you,"

they said. And they left their

and their and followed him.

One who loved was

Peter. He went everywhere with

 . Once he joined a great crowd

of people who had come to hear

 speak. The people would not

go home even though they were tired

and hungry. took a little boy's

supper of two and some small

 and suddenly there was

enough food to feed all the people.

No wonder Peter was astonished!

There was even enough left

over to fill twelve .

Sometimes talked about

going to heaven. He told Peter and

his friends that he would not be with

them for long.

The day came when said he

must go to Jerusalem and his friends

found a for him to ride. The

crowds were so happy to see

they waved in the air and

greeted him with shouts of joy. But

had enemies in Jerusalem who were plotting to kill him.

That same week came to the quiet little garden where was praying. The took him away and put him in prison. His enemies saw to it that was sentenced to die on the

The day died on the